Meltrek

Exploring Ancient Africa Storybook

Written By: Isaiah Lewis

To Pop Pop

The consistent man in my life

Now you are gone

I'm glad I made you proud

Ring! Ring! Ring! The school bell rings. The rowdy children begin storming into Ms. Loften's class and take their seats. Michelle, a pretty fashionista, is texting on her cell phone. Percy, a young scholar, is reading a book. Bunchie, a popular basketball player, and Chen, a cool skateboarder, are throwing paper balls at each other. Jessie, a popular cheerleader, is looking at herself in the mirror. Ms. Loften calms the room and grabs the attention of the children by simply saying, "quiet."

CHEN   PERCY   MICHELLE   JESSIE   BUNCHIE

"Can anyone name one of the ancient African civilizations?" asks Ms. Loften. There is a short pause. It appears no one can answer the question. Percy complains, "Why do we need to learn history?" Ms. Loften responds, "Well Percy, if you do not know where you come from then..." "You do not know where you are going" says the class in unison. "Also, history shapes how we view ourselves and the world" says Ms. Loften.

Objective: To learn about Ancient Africa civilizations.

Ring! Ring! Ring! The school bell signals the end of class. As the students begin to leave, Ms. Loften shouts "Bunchie, Percy, Michelle, Chen and Jessie please stay for a moment." Walking toward Ms. Loften Michelle asks, "Did we do something wrong?"
Ms. Loften replies, "No Michelle. I kept you after class to give you a further understanding of what we talked about today."

"Now," says Ms. Loften as she raises her arms, "take a seat, open your minds and let me take your mind on a journey, journey, journey...." The room begins to shake, objects move and the hands on the classroom clock spin backward. Mystical winds surround the children. A journey whirlwind has arrived to take the children on a meltrek.

The journey whirlwind takes the children to a mysterious land and places them alongside a beautiful river with reflections from the sun shining brightly in the sky. "What happened guys? Where are we?" exclaims Percy in a frantic tone. Bunchie replies "Chill with the questions Percy. We know just as little as you do."

Unexpectedly, the children are approached by a teenage boy with braids, wearing a white tunic. "Hotep, my name is Rameses. I was named in honor of Ramses II. What are your names?". One by one, the children introduce themselves. Percy explains he was named in honor of Huey P. Newton, Bunchie states that he was named after Bunchy Carter, and Michelle tells Rameses that she was named after Michelle Obama.

"What is the name of this land?" asks Michelle. "Africa, the birthplace of humanity!" Rameses proudly replies. "Where is Africa?" asks Percy. Rameses pulls a scroll, made of **papyrus**, from his pocket. He unrolls the scroll which displays a world map. "Here", says Rameses while pointing to Africa on the map. "It is the second largest continent in the world and we are beside the Nile River, the largest river in the world."

"Allow me to show you my land," says Rameses. The children agree and the group begins to venture along a pathway beside the Nile River. "Rameses, where are we going?" asks Chen. Rameses replies, "We are going to explore several places in Africa. Our first stop will be **Kemet**, daughter of the south, land of the black".

When the children arrive in Kemet, Rameses takes them to Lower Kemet to see the Step Pyramid located in Saqqara. The children are amazed by the enormous size of the pyramid. "This structure was designed by Imhotep during the reign of King Djoser and it is comprised of six mastabas," explains Rameses.

Imhotep

11

Next, Rameses takes the children to see the pyramids in Giza. While the other children gaze in awe at the pyramids, Percy turns to Rameses and asks, "How did the people of Kemet build pyramids without using modern technology?" Rameses answers, "They used their knowledge of mathematics and science to construct the pyramids. These people understood astronomy so well that many of the pyramids are aligned with certain stars."

The group departs Giza and is led by Rameses to the Hall of Pharaohs which is located in Onu, a major city located in Lower Kemet. "Rameses, what is this?" asks Jessie, as the children stare at the mysterious symbols on the wall. "This is our writing system called Medu Neter," explains Rameses. "What does it say?" asks Percy. "The Medu Neter says I know what is in my heart, which is the same as knowing yourself," responds Rameses.

They enter the Hall of Pharaohs. As Rameses guides the children down a narrow walkway, they see gigantic statues against the walls of the room. Rameses explains, "These are all of the rulers of Kemet from the 1st to the 30th dynasty." Pointing to a head made of stone resting on a short pillar, Michelle asks, "Who is that Rameses?" Rameses explains, "This is King Narmer, the first ruler of the first dynasty of Kemet."

Rameses guides the children to another room filled with large statues of pharaohs. The group first sees a large golden statue of a teenage-looking pharaoh. Michelle asks "Who is this? He looks young". Rameses responds, "This is King Tut. He was about your age when he began his reign." While the other children gaze at the statue, Bunchie thinks to himself, "I guess you are never too young to be poweful".

After moving to the next statue, Rameses says, "This is King Hatshepsut, one of the most powerful female kings. She expanded trade and oversaw impressive building projects". While Bunchie, Percy, Chen and Jessie stare in amazement at the statue, Michelle thinks to herself, "If she can rule a nation, I can rule one too".

Next, they see a statue of King Tutmose III. "Tutmose III was the nephew of King Hatshepsut. He was an amazing warrior-king who greatly expanded Kemet," explains Rameses. The children start asking Rameses questions about the adventures of Tutmose III. Meanwhile, Percy thinks to himself, "With proper training, practice and courage, I too can be a warrior-king".

As the children walk a little further, they see another large statue. "This is King Akhenaten. He worshipped the deity Aten and required his people to do the same," explains Rameses. While the other children observe the statue, Bunchie's imagination runs wild about becoming a powerful king one day.

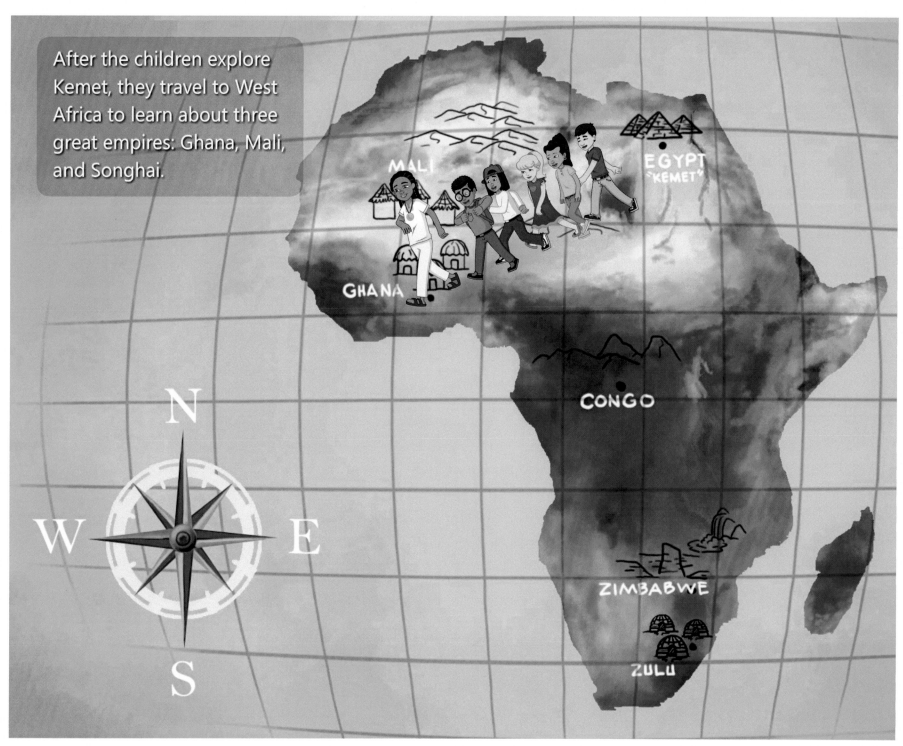

After the children explore Kemet, they travel to West Africa to learn about three great empires: Ghana, Mali, and Songhai.

19

When the children arrive in Ghana, they are shocked to see the enormous amounts of gold being transported by carriers. "Wow, that is a lot of gold", Michelle says to Rameses. The rest of the children nod in agreement. Rameses explains, "Ghana is known as the Gold Coast because this land is filled with gold. The people of Ghana often trade their gold to acquire unique goods from other nations."

Next, Rameses leads the children to the kingdom of Mali. While in Mali, they visit three cities: Djenne, Gao and lastly Timbuktu. Rameses explains, "Many people travel to these cities to attend the great centers of learning and to trade their unique goods." Chen says to the group, "These cities remind me of the large cities in our country like New York and Los Angeles where lots of trade occurs".

While in Timbuktu the group visits The Great Library. This building contains sacred books and scrolls written by scholars from all over the continent of Africa. The sacred texts discuss various topics such as science, mathematics, history, philosophy and more.

The Great Library

The group enters The Great Library and sees rows of bookcases filled with books and scrolls. Rameses walks the children to a bookcase, scans a shelf and pulls from it a huge book called *The Dawn of Ghana to the Fall of Songhai*. "This book lists all of the West African rulers and is rare because in West Africa history is traditionally preserved and taught by griots," says Rameses.

Rameses opens the heavy book, turns to a page and reads aloud "When Sundiata Keita ruled Mali, he led his army to many war victories that expanded the empire". "He was a great military leader just like Tutmose III" says Rameses.

Rameses turns the page and reads aloud about the nephew of Sundiata Keita, Mansa Musa. "He was an extremely wealthy king. He gave away a lot of gold as charity, especially during his hajj to Mecca," says Rameses. "Why did he go to Mecca?" asks Jessie. Rameses replies, "Mansa Musa was a devout Muslim and this was customary for his religion."

Rameses turns a few pages and displays two of the most powerful rulers in the history of Songhai. "To the left is a picture of Sonni Ali, the founder of Songhai. To the right is an image of his successor, Askia Muhammad". He continues "Sonni Ali expanded Songhai by taking over the land of the fallen empire of Mali. Askia Muhammad expanded Songhai, making it the largest empire in Africa during his time. He also created new laws based on the Quran".

Sonni Ali

Askia Muhammad

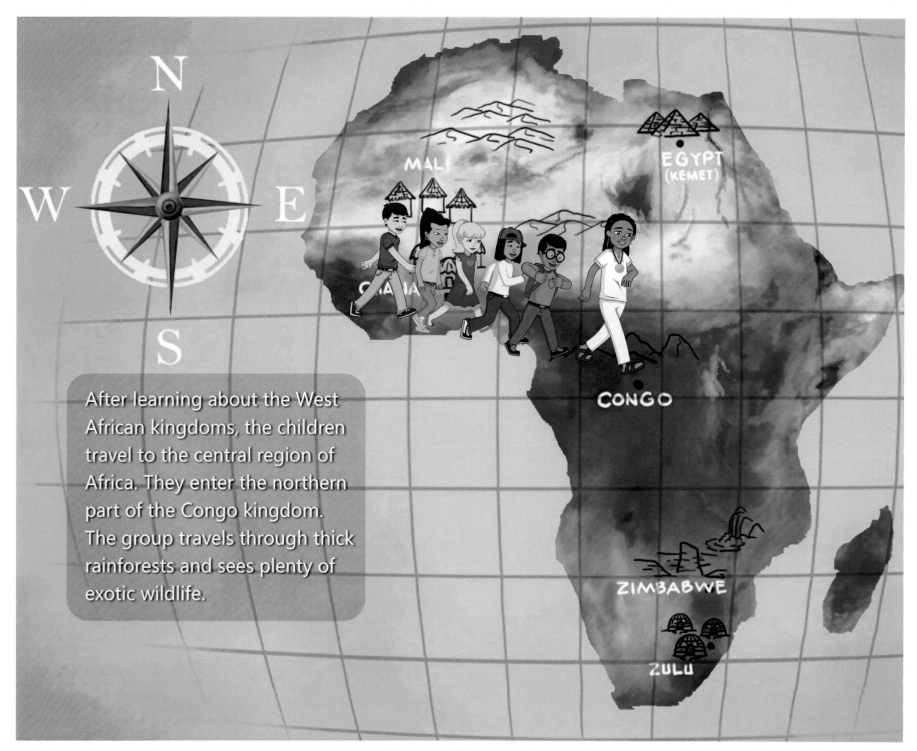

After learning about the West African kingdoms, the children travel to the central region of Africa. They enter the northern part of the Congo kingdom. The group travels through thick rainforests and sees plenty of exotic wildlife.

While in the forest, the children see a group of petite people gathering food. Percy asks, "Who are they?" pointing to the people. "They are the Twa people," says Rameses. "The Twa people are thought to be the oldest group of people inhabiting central Africa and are successful hunter-gatherers."

The group leaves the Congo region and travels south to Zimbabwe. When they reach the south-eastern hills of Zimbabwe, they see a gigantic stone structure. "Wow! What is that?" asks Chen while pointing to the structure. "This is the Great Enclosure built by the people of Great Zimbabwe. They are master stone masons.

The last stop on the journey was South Africa. Rameses introduces the children to members of the Zulu Nation who tell them stories about their fearless warrior-king named Shaka Zulu. They explain how Shaka rose to power and expanded their nation by conquering many tribes. "How did he defeat those tribes?" asks Bunchie. "Shaka created new battle tactics that gave his warriors an edge over their enemies", explains Rameses.

Rameses takes the children back to the starting point of their adventure. "I hope you enjoyed exploring my land! Now, I must go," says Rameses. "But we want to learn more," Percy says with excitement. Rameses leaves the children with these last words before he departs, "Continue to learn and seek the truth, for it will set you free." The children say their goodbyes and thank Rameses for his guidance.

"We have been traveling all day without one sip of water," complains Jessie. "And it is so hot here," adds Chen as he wipes sweat from his forehead. "Let's drink from the Nile River," suggests Percy. The children rush to the riverbank, dip their hands into the clear flowing water and begin to drink.

Powerful winds surround the children. A large white and black clock appears amidst the winds. The hands of the clock are spinning forward. The journey whirlwind has returned to transport the children back to the present. The children join hands and depart Africa. Although this is the end of their journey, the lessons learned during their meltrek will never be forgotten.

The journey whirlwind returns the children to the beginning of Ms. Loften's class. They are in their assigned seats, this time ready to learn. Ms. Loften asks the class, "Can anyone name one of the ancient kingdoms of Africa?" Percy, Bunchie, Jessie, Chen and Michelle raise their hands with excitement.

Ms. Loften first calls on Percy, who tells the class about Kemet and Imhotep. Michelle speaks about Ghana and its enormous gold trade. Jessie talks about the great rulers of Mali and Songhai. Chen shares what he knows about the Congo region and the Twa people. Lastly, Bunchie tells the class about Zimbabwe, Shaka Zulu and the Zulu Nation.

Ring! Ring! Ring! The school bell rings signaling the end of class. Bunchie, Jessie, Percy, Chen and Michelle meet at the doorway to talk. They each share their experience in Africa. However, they all believe their journey was a dream. Before the children exit the classroom Ms. Loften says, "Hotep," followed by a wink, a clear sign that their journey was real. The children are surprised, yet they simply reply, "Hotep Ms. Loften."

Objective: To learn about Ancient Africa civilizations.

Glossary

Akhenaten (lived during the 14th century b.c.e): Originally named Amenhotep IV and later renamed himself Akhenaten. Ruled during 18th dynasty of Kemet. Some historians say that he introduced the worship of one deity (monotheism). However, this was already practiced prior to his reign.

Askia Muhammad (Mohamed Toure) (born 1443 - died 1538): A ruler of the Songhai empire. He was devout muslim who expanded Songhai, making it the largest empire in Africa at that time. Askia Muhammad also created new laws based on his Islamic values.

Bunchy Carter (born 1942-1969): Born Alprentice Carter. He was a social activist and founding member of the South Carolina chapter of the Black Panther Party, an organization founded to address problems in the black urban community during the 1960s. Some of which were poverty, unemployment, police brutality, poor health care and education.

Deity: A divine being worshipped as the controlling force of the world, some aspect of life or the personification of a natural force or object.

Djoser (born circa 2650 b.c.e - died 2675 b.c.e): First ruler of the 3rd dynasty of Kemet. He was the first ruler to commission structures to be built using stones. One of which was his tomb, the Step Pyramid. This pyramid still stands in fair condition today.

Glossary

Dynasty: Occurs when one family rules a country or region over a long period of time. Generally, the head of the family will be the ruler of the land, such as an emperor or king. When that ruler dies, another member of the family assumes the position as ruler. When a new family takes control, a new dynasty begins.

Giza: Located in Lower Kemet. It has a plateau that contains three large pyramids and multiple smaller ones that were built by Pharaohs Khufu, Khafre and Menkaure from (2550 to 2490 b.c.e).

Great Enclosure: Located in Great Zimbabwe, a medieval city in the southeastern hills of Zimbabwe founded by the Shona people, and dates to the 14th century. The structure is made of granite blocks and contains living quarters, a community area, and a narrow passage leading to a high conical tower.

Griot: Storytellers, historians and musicians in Africa. As a storyteller, the griot entertained villagers with mythical, heroic and moral stories. As a historian, the griot would track, recite and pass down the history of the village including births, deaths, marriages, droughts, wars and other important events. As a musician, the griot would play an instrument while singing or telling a story. Although griots were mostly men, a woman could also be a griot. Another word for griot is "jeli".

Hajj: A religious journey to Mecca that all Muslims, who are physically and financially capable, are expected to make at least once in their lifetime.

Glossary

Hatshepsut (born circa 1508 b.c.e - died 1458 b.c.e): A ruler during the 18th dynasty. She extended trade and oversaw impressive building projects, most particularly the Temple of Deir el-Bahri, located in western Thebes (Upper Kemet). She, along with other female rulers, were referred to as "king" because in Kemet "king" is considered a position of office that can be held by a male or female.

Hotep: Several meanings exist for this term. However, the primary definitions are "peace" and "offerings".

Huey P. Newton (born 1942 - died 1989): Co-founder and leader of the Black Panther Party for Self-defense, and became a leading figure in the Black Power movement of the 1960s.

Imhotep (born circa 2667 b.c.e - died 2600 b.c.e): Architect, astrologer, doctor, mathematician and chief minister of King Djoser during the 3rd dynasty. He was responsible for designing the Step Pyramid. Imhotep was later exalted as the deity of medicine in both Kemet and Greece.

Kemet: Sometimes spelled "kmt" is the ancient name for Egypt. It means "the black land".

Lower Kemet: Kemet was divided into two regions, namely Lower Kemet and Upper Kemet. Lower Kemet is the northern part of Kemet where the Nile River empties into the Mediterranean Sea. Upper Kemet is the southern part of Kemet.

Glossary

Mansa Musa (born 1280 - died 1337): Born Musa Keita. He became "Mansa" (which means emperor) of Mali around 1312. Mansa Musa was the tenth emperor of the Keita dynasty and is regarded as the richest man to ever live. Forbes magazine estimated that his net worth, according to today's standard, was $400 billion dollars. During his hajj he gave away large amounts of gold. His gold disrupted the economies in several places.

Mastaba: A rectangular tomb, initially built using mud brick and later stone, used by the people of Kemet to bury their deceased. It contained a deep shaft that descended to an underground burial chamber where the coffin was located. The people of Kemet viewed a mastaba as an "Eternal House" or "House of Eternity".

Medu Neter: Translated as "divine words", is an ancient writing system developed by the people of Kemet. It is comprised of signs and symbols of nature. Greeks referred to the Medu Neter as hieroglyphics, the term commonly used for it today.

Meltrek: A journey back in time to explore the history, culture and achievements of African people.

Michelle Obama (born 1964-present): Born in Chicago, Illinois, she grew up to become a highly educated lawyer and First Lady of the United States from 2009 to 2017. Her husband, Barack Obama, is the 44th President of the United States. As First Lady she took on several causes. Some were childhood obesity, veteran rights, and higher education.

Glossary

Narmer (lived during the 32nd century b.c.e): Also known as Menes, united Upper and Lower Kemet into one kingdom and became the first ruler of the 1st dynasty.

Onu: An ancient Kemetic city. It was an important religious center that contained a large temple dedicated to Ra, a sun deity. The priest of Onu became the most influential when Ra became the national deity during the fifth dynasty.

Papyrus: A plant that grows along the Nile River. The people of Kemet used papyrus to make paper, baskets, sandals, mats, rope, blankets, tables, chairs, mattresses, medicine, perfume, food, and clothes.

Ramses II (born circa 1292 b.c.e - died 1190 b.c.e): Full name was Ursa Maat Ra Setep En Ra Ramessu Meri Amen. He was the third ruler of the 19th dynasty of Kemet and is regarded as one of the greatest rulers. He had lots of military successes and constructed many temples during his reign. Both are indications that the empire was prosperous under his rule.

Shaka Zulu (born circa 1787- died 1828): Notable ruler and military leader of the Zulu Nation, a tribe that dwelled in South Africa. Shaka created new war strategies that led to many war victories for the Zulu Nation. Some included using a shorter staff for close range combat and the buffalo formation. The latter is a strategy that involved four groups of soldiers. One group was assigned to attack the enemy head on; two groups were instructed to surround and attack the enemy; and a fourth group of soldiers were on reserve.

Glossary

Sonni Ali (lived during the 15th century): Born Ali Kolon. He became the first ruler of the Songhai empire in 1464. He initiated Songhai's rise to power by conquering the most important West African trading centers, first the city of Timbuktu and later the city of Djenne.

Sundiata Keita (born 1190 - died 1225): Founder and first ruler of Mali. His army expanded Mali, making it one of the most powerful empires in West Africa. Sundiata was a Muslim, however, he still participated in traditional religious practices with his non-Muslim citizens.

Tunic: A simple long garment that slips on and hangs near the knees. It was commonly worn during ancient times and is still worn in certain places today.

Tutankhamen (born circa 1343 b.c.e. - died 1324 b.c.e): Commonly called King Tut. He was the youngest ruler of Kemet. During his reign the majority of the royal decisions were made by his advisors, until his early death at the age of 19. He is mostly known for his tomb, which was well in tact when it was discovered in the Valley of the Kings (located in Upper Kemet) by Howard Carter in 1922.

Tutmose III (born circa 1492 - died 1426 b.c.e): One of the rulers during the 18th dynasty of Kemet. He was a warrior-king who expanded Kemet north into the middle east where he conquered all of Syria. He also stretched Kemet further south along the Nile River to Napata in the Sudan. He commissioned the building of many temples and monuments to celebrate his achievements.

Glossary

Twa: Also called the Batwa, they are believed to be the descendants of the original inhabitants of equatorial Africa. The Twa people are known to have dwelled in several areas, primarily the Congo, Rwanda and Burundi. They were small people who averaged five feet in height.

Quran: The religious doctrine of the Islamic faith. Believed to be the word of Allah (Arabic word for "God") revealed by the Archangel Gabriel and written down by the Prophet Muhammad.

Note: The term, "circa" means approximately, around or about - used especially with dates.

Bibliography

1. Browder, Anthony T. *Nile Valley Contributions to Civilization*. Washington, D.C.: Institute of Karmic Guidance, 1992. Print.

2. Diop, Cheikh Anta., and Harold Salemson. *Precolonial Black Africa*. N.p.: Chicago Review, 1988. Print.

3. BBen-Jochannan, Yosef. *Black Man of the Nile and His Family*. 256. Baltimore, MD: Black Classic, 1989. Print.

4. David, Saul. *The Illustrated Encyclopedia of Warfare: From Ancient Egypt to Iraq*. 246. New York: DK Pub., 2012. Print.

5. Jenkins, Everett. *The Muslim Diaspora: A Comprehensive Chronology of the Spread of Islam in Asia, Africa, Europe, and the Americas*. 217. Jefferson, NC: McFarland, 2011. Print.

6. Goodwin, Stefan. *Africa's Legacies of Urbanization: Unfolding Saga of a Continent*. 96. Lanham, MD: Lexington, 2006. Print.

Bibliography

7. Imhotep, *Asar. Nsw.t Bjt.j (King) In Ancient Egyptian:: A Lesson in Paronymy and Leadership*. Philadelphia: Madu-Ndela Press, 2016. Print.

8. Remler, Pat. *Egyptian Mythology* A to Z: A Young Reader's Companion. 77,78. New York, NY: Facts on File, 2000. Print.

9. Alexander, Leslie M., and Walter C. Rucker. *Encyclopedia of African American History*. 102. Santa Barbara, Calif.: ABC-CLIO, 2010. Print.

10. Mokhtar, G. *Ancient Civilizations of Africa*. 266.London: Heinemann, 1981. Print.